Everyday Mathematics®

The University of Chicago School Mathematics Project

Skills Link

Cumulative Practice Sets
Student Book

McGraw Hill Wright Group

The McGraw·Hill Companies

Photo Credits

Cover—Getty Images, cover, *right*; Frank Lane Picture Agency/CORBIS, cover, *bottom left*; ©Star/sefa/CORBIS, cover, *center*

Photo Collage—Herman Adler Design

www.WrightGroup.com

 **Wright Group**

Send all inquiries to:
Wright Group/McGraw-Hill
P.O. Box 812960
Chicago, IL 60681

ISBN 978-0-07-618785-0
MHID 0-07-618785-3

3 4 5 6 7 8 9 WDQ 13 12 11 10

Contents

Practice Set 1

Use with or after
Lesson 1·4

Add.

1. _____   2. _____

Fill in the missing numbers.

3.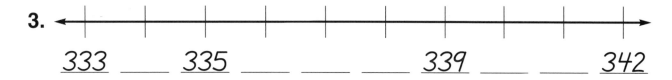

_333_   ___   _335_   ___   ___   ___   _339_   ___   ___   _342_

4.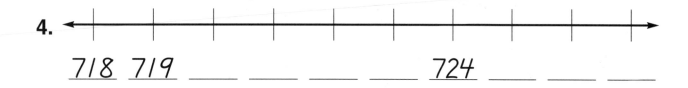

_718_ _719_ ___   ___   ___   _724_   ___   ___

Draw the hands to show the time.

5.    6.    7.

7:00   10:30   3:15

Practice Set 2

Use with or after
Lesson 1·7

MRB
22–24
88–89

Find the sum.

Unit
puppies

1. 3
  + 3

2. 2
  + 1

3. 0
  + 6

4. 4
  + 2

5. ____ = 3 + 2   **6.** 1 + 4 = ____   **7.** ____ = 2 + 2

8. 3 + 0 = ____   **9.** ____ = 4 + 5   **10.** 2 + 5 = ____

Write the total amount.

Example   = __61__ ¢

11.   = ____ ¢

12.   = ____ ¢

13.   = ____ ¢

How many?

14. ____ = 2   **15.** 1 = ____

Practice Set 3

~~501~~	502	~~503~~	504				508		510
511				515				519	
	522					527			530
531					536		538		
541			544					549	
	552	553							560
				565	566				
571	572						577		579
		583	584						590
591			594				597		599	600
		603							609	
611									620

1. Fill in all of the missing numbers on the grid.

2. Now start at 501 and count by 2s.
   Put an **X** over each number as you count.

3. Now start at 510 and count by 10s.
   Color each number **blue** as you count.

4. Color the number that is 1 more than 513 **red.**

5. Color the number that is 5 more than 601 **green.**

3

Practice Set 4

Use with or after
Lesson 1·9

Finish these names for 11:

Unit
kittens

1. __5__ + _____ = 11

2. __4__ + _____ = 11

3. __3__ + _____ = 11

4. _____ + __2__ = 11

How much money? Write the amount.

5.

$_____

6.

$_____

7.

$_____._____

Practice Set 5

Use with or after
Lesson 1·10

Use your calculator to count.

To count by 2s	To count by 5s	To count by 10s
Press ② and ⊕. Then press ⊜ over and over.	Press ⑤ and ⊕. Then press ⊜ over and over.	Press ① ⓪ and ⊕. Then press ⊜ over and over.

1. Count by 2s using your calculator. Write the numbers.

   _2_ , _4_ , _6_ , ____ , ____ , ____ , ____ , ____ , ____

2. Count by 5s using your calculator. Write the numbers.

   _5_ , _10_ , _15_ , ____ , ____ , ____ , ____ , ____ , ____

3. Count by 10s using your calculator. Write the numbers.

   _10_ , _20_ , ____ , ____ , ____ , ____ , ____ , ____ , ____

Match.

4. seven dollars and twenty-seven cents $2.17

5. seventy-two cents $7.02

6. two dollars and seventeen cents $0.72

7. seven dollars and two cents $7.27

8. two dollars and seventy cents $2.70

Practice Set 6

Use with or after
Lesson 1·11

Use <, >, or =.

< means *is less than*
> means *is greater than*
= means *is the same as*

1. 49 ___ 94

2. 347 ___ 374

3. 10 ___ 3 + 6

4. 921 ___ 919

5. 9 − 4 ___ 4

6. 3 + 3 ___ 10 − 5

7. 3 + 4 ___ 1 + 6

Count by 5s.

8. _5_ , _10_ , ___ , ___ , ___ , _30_ , ___ , ___ , _45_

9. _65_ , ___ , ___ , ___ , ___ , ___ , ___ , _100_ , ___

10. _120_ , _125_ , ___ , ___ , ___ , ___ , ___ , ___ , _160_

11. _250_ , ___ , ___ , ___ , ___ , ___ , ___ , _285_ , ___

12. Fill in the missing numbers.

351	352	353	354						360
	362		365						
371		373				377	378		380
		384						389	

6

Practice Set 7

Write the number.

1.

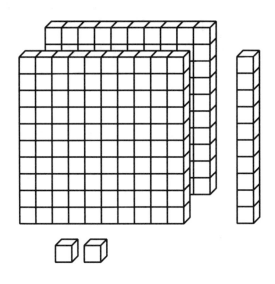

_____

2.

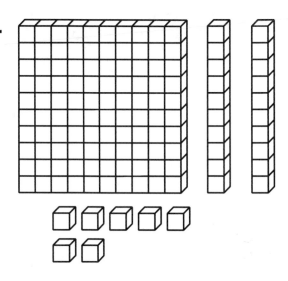

_____

Fill in the blanks.

Example 376 = __3__ hundreds __7__ tens __6__ ones

3. 923 = _____ hundreds _____ tens _____ ones

4. 485 = _____ hundreds _____ tens _____ ones

5. 709 = _____ hundreds _____ tens _____ ones

6. 626 = _____ hundreds _____ tens _____ ones

7. 247 = _____ hundreds _____ tens _____ ones

Count by 10s.

8. _100_, _110_, ____, ____, ____, _150_, ____, ____, _180_

9. _220_, ____, _240_, ____, ____, ____, _280_, ____, _300_

Practice Set 8

Use with or after Lesson 2·1

1. Write an addition story that asks a question.

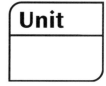

Unit

_____

_____

_____

Answer the question: _____

Write a number model: _____ + _____ = _____

2. Show $0.75 three ways. Use Qs, Ds, and Ns.

8

Practice Set 9

Use with or after
Lesson 2·3

Add. Use the Facts Table on journal page 26.

1. $4 + 4 =$ _____   **2.** $7 + 7 =$ _____   **3.** $8 + 8 =$ _____

4. $\begin{array}{r} 9 \\ +9 \\ \hline \end{array}$ **5.** $\begin{array}{r} 8 \\ +9 \\ \hline \end{array}$ **6.** $\begin{array}{r} 7 \\ +6 \\ \hline \end{array}$ **7.** $\begin{array}{r} 6 \\ +5 \\ \hline \end{array}$

Circle the correct time.

8.

7:15   6:30

9.

6:00   12:30

Write the number.

Unit
marshmallows

Example three hundred fifty-two _352_

10. eight hundred twenty-nine _____

11. two hundred seventeen _____

12. seven hundred nine _____

13. ninety-one _____

Practice Set 10

Use with or after
Lesson 2-4

Write the turn-around addition facts for each domino.

Example

$6 + 3 = 9$

$3 + 6 = 9$

1.  _____

_____

2. 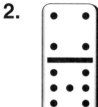 _____

_____

3.  _____

_____

Count back by 10s.

4. 200, 190, 180, ____, ____, ____, ____, ____, 120

5. 350, 340, ____, ____, ____, ____, 290, ____, ____

6. 620, 610, ____, ____, 580, ____, ____, ____, ____

7. 470, ____, ____, ____, ____, ____, ____, ____, 390

8. Write today's date.

_____ _____, _____
    (month)   (day)   (year)

Practice Set 11

Use with or after
Lesson 2·6

1. Write 4 number sentences to match the picture.

Unit

_____ + _____ = _____   _____ − _____ = _____

_____ + _____ = _____   _____ − _____ = _____

Subtract.

2. 4 − 0 = _____   **3.** 7 − 1 = _____   **4.** 8 − 0 = _____

5. 12   **6.** 10   **7.** 7   **8.** 6
   − 1   − 9   − 0   − 1

---

9. A teddy bear is on sale for $4.99. A stuffed alligator costs $5.19.

Which item costs more?

_____

10. A bunch of bananas costs $3.45. A bag of apples costs $7.00.

Which item costs less?

_____

Practice Set 12

Use with or after
Lesson 2-7

Write the fact family for the Fact Triangle.

Example

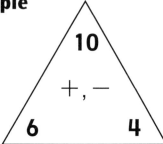

1.

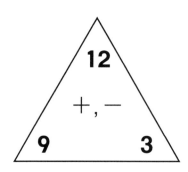

$6 + 4 = 10$

$4 + 6 = 10$

$10 - 6 = 4$

$10 - 4 = 6$

___ + ___ = ___

___ + ___ = ___

___ − ___ = ___

___ − ___ = ___

---

2. Show 57¢ two different ways.

3. Show 81¢ two different ways.

12

Name   Date   Time

Practice Set 13

Use with or after
Lesson 2-9

1. Write 5 names for the number.

Example

10	16
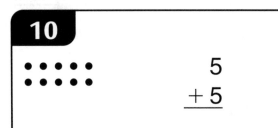 5 + 5 8 + 2 11 − 1 //// ////	

Write the fact family for each domino.

2.

6 + 2 = ____

2 + 6 = ____

8 − 6 = ____

8 − 2 = ____

3.

3 + 4 = ____

4 + 3 = ____

7 − 3 = ____

7 − 4 = ____

13

Practice Set 14

Use with or after
Lesson 2·10

Fill in the frames.

1. 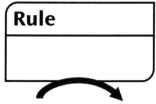 Rule

| 8 | 14 | 20 | | |

2. Rule

25

Fill in the arrow rule.

3. 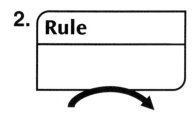 Rule

82 84 86 88 90

4. 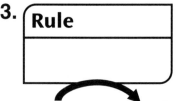 Rule

67 57 47 37 27

Count back by 10s.

5. 450, 440, ____, ____, ____, ____, ____, ____, ____

6. 92, 82, ____, ____, ____, ____, ____, ____, 12

7. 137, ____, ____, ____, 97, ____, ____, ____, ____

Practice Set 15

Complete the table.

1.

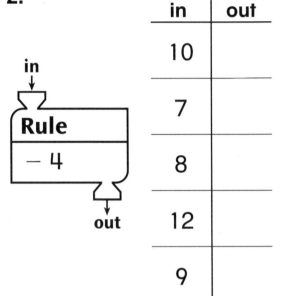

in	out
6	11
8	13
9	
3	
7	

2.

in	out
10	
7	
8	
12	
9	

Tell if the number is *even* or *odd*.

3. 7 _____   4. 19 _____   5. 6 _____

6. 42 _____   7. 67 _____   8. 94 _____

9. Write three *even* numbers between 50 and 100.

    ____ ____ ____

10. Write three *odd* numbers between 50 and 100.

    ____ ____ ____

11. Write a 3-digit number that has ...
    an even number in the hundreds place
    an odd number in the tens place
    an odd number in the ones place   _____

Name _____ Date _____ Time _____

Use with or after
Lesson 2-12

Subtract.

Unit
stickers

1. $9 - 7 =$ _____

2. $12 - 7 =$ _____   3. $10 - 8 =$ _____

4. $\begin{array}{r} 16 \\ -9 \\ \hline \end{array}$ 5. $\begin{array}{r} 14 \\ -9 \\ \hline \end{array}$ 6. $\begin{array}{r} 13 \\ -6 \\ \hline \end{array}$ 7. $\begin{array}{r} 11 \\ -5 \\ \hline \end{array}$

8. $\begin{array}{r} 16 \\ -10 \\ \hline \end{array}$ 9. $\begin{array}{r} 24 \\ -10 \\ \hline \end{array}$ 10. $\begin{array}{r} 31 \\ -10 \\ \hline \end{array}$ 11. $\begin{array}{r} 17 \\ -10 \\ \hline \end{array}$

**Write the missing number in the triangle.
Then write the fact family.**

12.

13.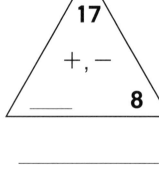

14.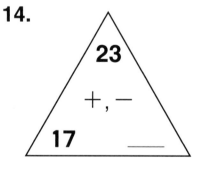

16

Practice Set 17

Write the 3-digit number that has ...

Example

8 in the hundreds place

4 in the tens place

6 in the ones place

__846__

1. 5 in the hundreds place

2 in the tens place

0 in the ones place

_____

2. 4 in the hundreds place

9 in the tens place

3 in the ones place

_____

3. 2 in the hundreds place

7 in the tens place

8 in the ones place

_____

Label the box. Then add four new names.

Example

9

$10 - 1$

$\begin{array}{r} 8 \\ + 1 \\ \hline \end{array}$

卌 ////

$4 + 5$ $6 + 3$

$\begin{array}{r} 8 \\ + 1 \\ \hline \end{array}$ $\begin{array}{r} 9 \\ + 0 \\ \hline \end{array}$

4.

$6 + 6$ $13 - 1$

$3 + 9$

Practice Set 18

How many?

1. 3 = _____

2. _____ = 2

3. _____ 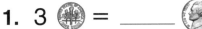 = 1

4. 2 = _____

5. 1 = _____ and _____

Use the digits. Write the largest and smallest numbers.

Digits	Smallest Number	Largest Number
6. 9, 2, 7		
7. 1, 8, 5		
8. 3, 4, 6		
9. 7, 2, 7		

Find the difference.

Unit
toys

10. _____ = 6 − 3   11. 7 − 5 = _____

12. 9 − 4 = _____   13. _____ = 4 − 2   14. 10 − 3 = _____

15.   3   16.   8   17.   9   18.   7   19.   6
    − 2   − 5   − 3   − 0   − 1
   ____   ____   ____   ____   ____

Name _____ Date _____ Time _____

Practice Set 19

Use with or after
Lesson 3·3

Tell the time.

1.    **2.**

How much money?

3.

4.

Write >, <, or =.

5. 2 quarters ___ 5 dimes   **6.** 5 dimes ___ 7 nickels

7. 6 nickels ___ 35 cents   **8.** 4 quarters ___ $1.10

Name _____ Date _____ Time _____

Write the number.

1.

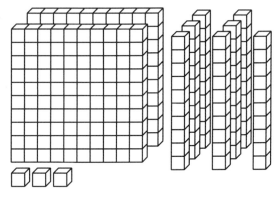

_____

2.

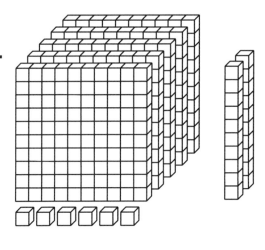

_____

How much money?

3.

$_____ . _____

4.

$_____ . _____

Circle the time that matches the clock face.

5.

6:10   1:30

6.

9:45   10:45

Practice Set 21

Fill in the frames.

1.

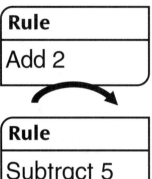
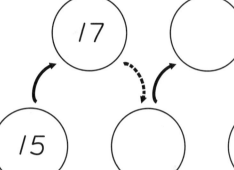

Rule
Add 2

Rule
Subtract 5

2.

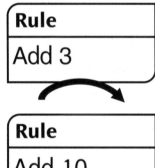
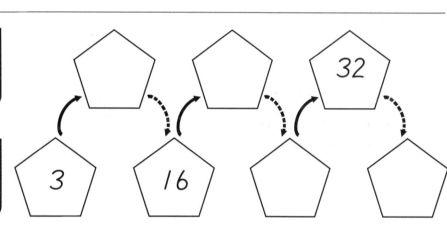

Rule
Add 3

Rule
Add 10

Write the number.

Unit
spiders

3. six hundred twenty-nine _____

4. two hundred ninety-six _____

5. nine hundred sixteen _____

6. six hundred twenty _____

7. four hundred thirty _____

Practice Set 22

Use with or after
Lesson 3·7

Time for Treats

40¢   20¢   8¢   18¢

Yogurt   Pretzels   Banana   Raisins

Count up to find out how much change you will get.

1. You buy a box of raisins. You give the clerk 2 dimes. How much change do you get?

_____

2. You buy the yogurt. You give the clerk 2 quarters. How much change do you get?

_____

3. You buy a banana. You give the clerk 1 dime. How much change do you get?

_____

4. You buy a bag of pretzels. You give the clerk 2 dimes. How much change do you get?

_____

Count by 2s.

5. _612_, _614_, ____, ____, ____, ____, ____, ____, ____, _630_

6. _371_, ____, _375_, ____, ____, ____, ____, ____, _387_, ____

Name _____ Date _____ Time _____

Practice Set 23

Use with or after Lesson 3·8

Show the least amount of coins you can use to buy each item. Draw Ⓠs, Ⓓs, Ⓝs, or Ⓟs.

1.
CRACKERS 43¢

2.
NUTS 62¢

3.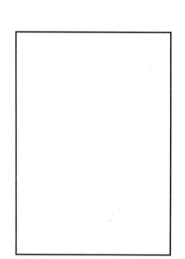
SUNFLOWER SEEDS 28¢

Count by 3s.

4. _3_, _6_, _9_, ___, ___, _18_, ___, ___, ___, _30_

5. _39_, _42_, ___, ___, ___, _54_, ___, ___, _63_, ___

6. _20_, _23_, ___, ___, ___, _35_, ___, ___, ___, _47_

7. _52_, ___, _58_, ___, ___, ___, _70_, ___, ___, _79_

8. _100_, _103_, _106_, ___, ___, ___, ___, ___, ___, _127_

23

Name _____ Date _____ Time _____

Practice Set 24

Use with or after
Lesson 4·1

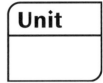

Fill in the unit box.
Then finish each diagram
and write a number model to go with it.

Unit

Example

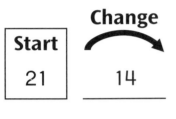

Change

Start		End
21	14	35

_____ 21 + 14 = 35 _____

1.

Change

Start		End
31	____	56

_____

2.

Change

Start		End
	45	91

_____

3.

Change

Start		End
66	27	

_____

Use the three digits.
Write the smallest and largest numbers.

Example

    3, 9, 1   smallest ___139___   largest ___931___

4. 4, 7, 6   smallest _____   largest _____

5. 2, 6, 3   smallest _____   largest _____

6. 8, 5, 9   smallest _____   largest _____

7. 4, 3, 6   smallest _____   largest _____

24

Practice Set 25

Answer the question and write a number model.

Example

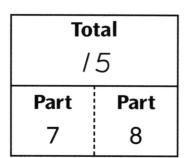

Total	
15	
Part	**Part**
7	8

$$7 + 8 = 15$$

1.

Total	
32	
Part	**Part**
21	?

_____

2.

Total	
61	
Part	**Part**
?	34

_____

3.

Total		
?		
Part	**Part**	**Part**
7	9	5

_____

What's your change?

4. You buy a package of crackers for 37 cents.
You give the clerk 2 quarters.

Your change: _____

5. Nuts cost 62 cents. You pay with 3 quarters.

Your change: _____

Practice Set 26

Color the thermometer to show the temperature.

Example

47°F

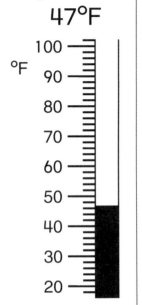

1. 59°F
2. 55°F
3. 62°F

Write the rule. Then fill in the table.

Example

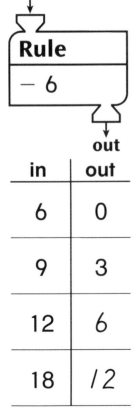

in	out
6	0
9	3
12	6
18	12

4.

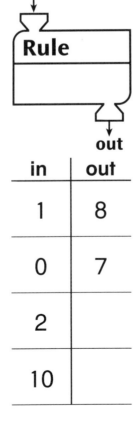

in	out
1	8
0	7
2	
10	

5.

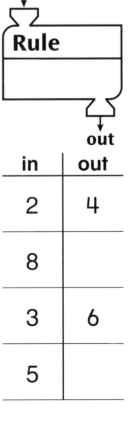

in	out
2	4
8	
3	6
5	

Practice Set 27

Use with or after
Lesson 4·4

Record the temperature.

Example	**1.**	**2.**	**3.**
8:00 A.M.	12:30 P.M.	5:00 P.M.	9:00 P.M.

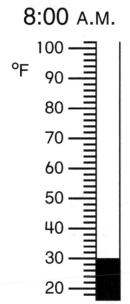 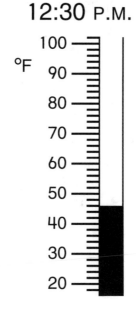 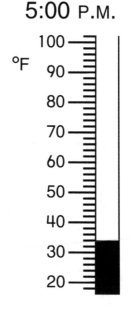 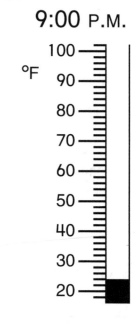

_30_ °F   _____°F   _____°F   _____°F

---

4. How much warmer is it at 12:30 P.M. than at 8:00 A.M.?

_____°F warmer

5. How much colder is it at 9:00 P.M. than at 5:00 P.M.?

_____°F colder

Fill in the unit box.
Then solve each problem.

Unit

6. 4 + 2 + 6 = ____   **7.** ____ = 7 + 2 + 7

8. ____ = 9 + 3 + 1   **9.** 8 + 4 + 5 = ____

10. 5 + 9 + 4 = ____   **11.** 7 + 8 + 3 = ____

Practice Set 28

How long is each line segment?

1.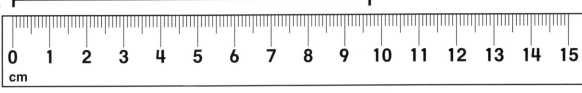

   = about _____ centimeters

2.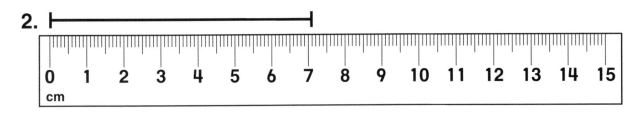

   = about _____ centimeters

3.

   = about _____ centimeters

Use these numbers to answer the questions below:

429   539   421   527   581

4. Which numbers have 9 ones? _____

5. Which numbers have 5 hundreds? _____

6. Which numbers have 2 tens? _____

7. Which numbers have 4 hundreds? _____

Practice Set 29

Use with or after
Lesson 4·9

Use the partial-sums method to solve the problems.

Unit

Example	10s	1s	
	5	7	
+	2	5	
	7	0	Add the tens (50 + 20 = 70).
+	1	2	Add the ones (7 + 5 = 12).
	8	2	Combine the tens and the ones (70 + 12 = 82).

1.   56
    + 37

2.   77
    + 17

3.   39
    + 53

4.   237
    + 154

How long is each line segment?

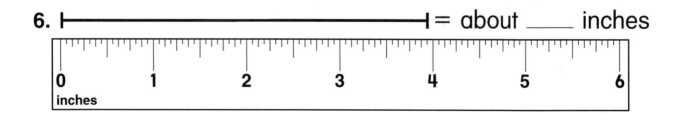

5. ├————————————┤ = about ____ inches

6. ├————————————————┤ = about ____ inches

Practice Set 30

Match.

1.

2.

3.

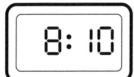

4.

Write two 3-digit numbers that have ...

5. 3 in the ones place

_____ , _____

6. 7 in the hundreds place

_____ , _____

7. 6 in the tens place

_____ , _____

8. 1 in the ones place and 0 in the tens place

_____ , _____

9. Now write six numbers using the digits 4, 9, and 2.

_____ , _____

_____ , _____

_____ , _____

Practice Set 31

**Use with or after
Lesson 5·3**

1. Find the figure on the right that has the same **shape** as the one below. Color it **red.**

2. Find the figure on the right that is almost the same **size** as the one below. Color it **blue.**

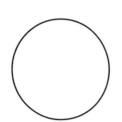

Use <, >, or =.

| < means *is less than* |
| > means *is greater than* |
| = means *is the same as* |

3. 473 ☐ 437

4. 4 + 5 ☐ 9

5. 55 ☐ 48 + 5   6. 87¢ ☐ $0.86

7. 5 nickels ____ 1 quarter   8. 4 + 66 ____ 66 + 40

31

Practice Set 32

Use with or after
Lesson 5·4

1.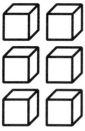

2.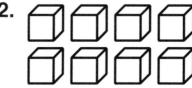

How many rows? _____

How many
in each row? _____

How many in all? _____

How many rows? _____

How many
in each row? _____

How many in all? _____

Use Qs, Ds, Ns, or Ps to show the coins you could use to buy each item.

3.  76¢

4. 58¢

5.  98¢

Practice Set 33

Write the name of each quadrangle.
Copy the name from journal page 120.

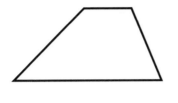 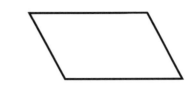 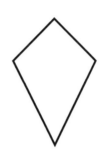

1. _____ **2.** _____ **3.** _____

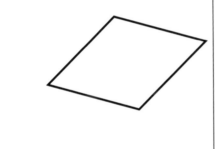 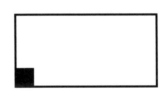 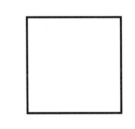

4. _____ **5.** _____ **6.** _____

7. Draw a black box to show each right angle.
   One box has been drawn for you in Figure 5.

8. Color each pair of parallel lines **green.**
   If a shape has more than one pair of parallel lines,
   color the second pair **yellow.**

Practice Set 34

Use with or after
Lesson 5·7

MRB
16
58–59

How many edges, faces, and vertices?

Example	**1.**	**2.**
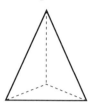	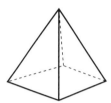	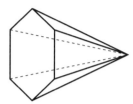
Triangular Pyramid	**Rectangular Pyramid**	**Hexagonal Pyramid**
Edges: _6_	Edges: _____	Edges: _____
Faces: _4_	Faces: _____	Faces: _____
Vertices: _4_	Vertices: _____	Vertices: _____

Write 8 names for each number.

3.
15

4.
18

Practice Set 35

Use with or after
Lesson 6·1

Fill in the unit box.
Then solve.

Unit

1. $15 + 5 + 2 =$ _____

2. $13 + 2 + 7 =$ _____

3. $6 + 50 + 25 =$ _____

4. $18 + 4 + 9 =$ _____

5. $21 + 9 + 1 =$ _____

6. $12 + 7 + 8 =$ _____

Write the fact family.

7.

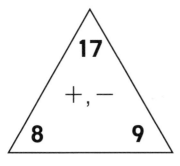

_____

_____

_____

_____

8.

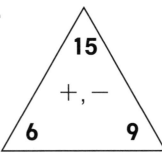

_____

_____

_____

_____

9.

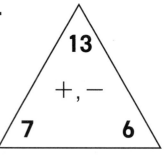

_____

_____

_____

_____

Write the fact family.

10. 9, 9, 18   ___ + ___ = ___   ___ − ___ = ___

11. 10, 5, 5   ___ + ___ = ___   ___ − ___ = ___

Practice Set 36

Fill in the unit box.
Then finish each diagram
and write a number model to go with it.

Unit

Example

Quantity
59

Quantity	
32	27
	Difference

$59 - 32 = 27$

1.

Quantity
86

Quantity	
	59
	Difference

_____

2.

Quantity
92

Quantity	
34	
	Difference

_____

3.

Quantity

Quantity	
14	56
	Difference

_____

Find the difference between the temperatures.

4. 34°C and 15°C

_____

5. 13°F and 67°F

_____

6. 95°F and 57°F

_____

7. 24°C and 9°C

_____

Practice Set 37

Use with or after
Lesson 6·3

MRB 40 44

1. Use the tally chart to finish the bar graph.

2. How many more second graders own a dog than a cat?

   _____ more 2nd graders

   A fish than a bird?

   _____ more 2nd graders

Pets Owned by Second Graders	
Cat	ℍℍ ℍℍ ℍℍ ℍℍ ℍℍ ////
Fish	ℍℍ ℍℍ ℍℍ //
Dog	ℍℍ ℍℍ ℍℍ ℍℍ ℍℍ ℍℍ ℍℍ ///
Bird	ℍℍ ///

Pets Owned by Second Graders

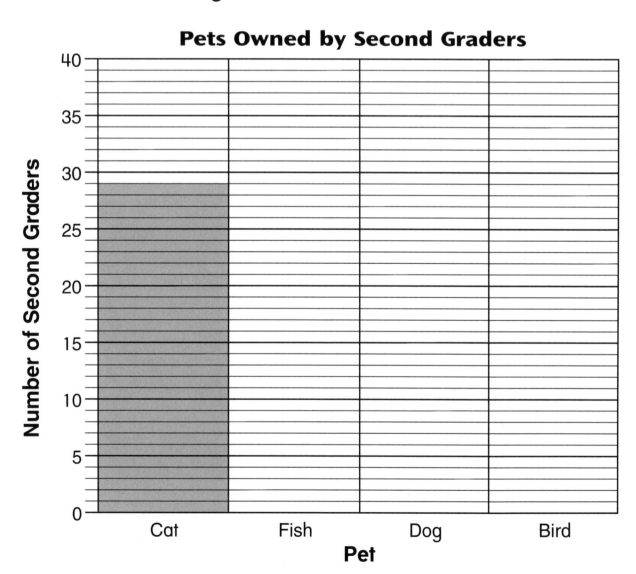

Number of Second Graders

Pet

37

Practice Set 38

Choose a diagram to help you solve each problem. Then solve the problem and write a number model to go with it.

1. One duck has 13 ducklings. Another duck has 12. How many ducklings are there in all?

   There are _____ ducklings in all.

   Number model:

   _____

2. 65 worker bees were in the hive. 23 of them flew away. How many worker bees are left in the hive?

   _____ worker bees are left in the hive.

   Number model:

   _____

3. 39 roses were blooming in the garden. Alberto picked 12 of them. How many roses were not picked?

   _____ roses were not picked.

   Number model:

   _____

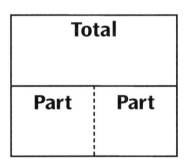

Practice Set 39

Use with or after
Lesson 6-5

**Make a ballpark estimate. Then subtract.
Trade first if you need to.**

1.

longs 10s	cubes 1s
5	/ /
6	1
−3	2

Answer

Ballpark estimate:

$60 - 30 = 30$

2.

longs 10s	cubes 1s
4	5
−1	7

Answer

Ballpark estimate:

_____

Fill in the arrow rule. Complete the frames.

3.
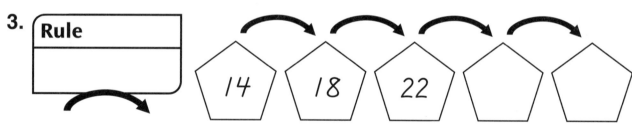

Rule
_____

14   18   22   ___   ___

4.
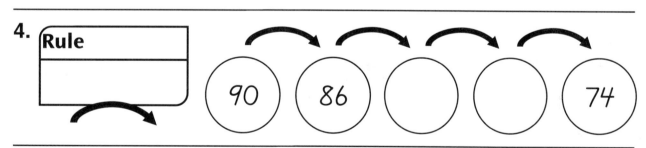

Rule
_____

90   86   ___   ___   74

5.
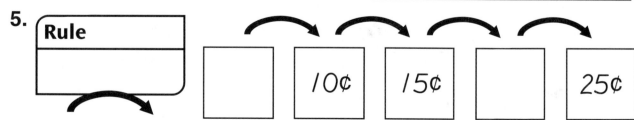

Rule
_____

___   10¢   15¢   ___   25¢

Practice Set 40

Use with or after
Lesson 6·7

1. How many rows? _____

   How many in each row? _____

   How many balls in all? _____

---

2. How many nuts in all? _____

   How many bowls? _____

   How many nuts in each bowl
   if each bowl gets same amount? _____

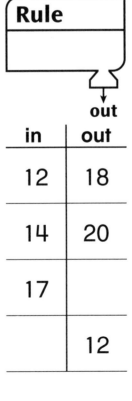

Write the rule. Then fill in the table.

3. in

Rule

out

in	out
20	30
70	80
	90
60	

4. in

Rule

out

in	out
24	16
38	30
16	
	20

5. in

Rule

out

in	out
12	18
14	20
17	
	12

Practice Set 41

1. Rosemary put 4 vases of flowers on the tables. Each vase has 5 flowers. How many flowers are there in all?

   Answer: _____ flowers

2. On Saturday, 6 children went fishing. Each child caught 4 fish. How many fish did the children catch in all?

   Answer: _____ fish

3. Dave has 2 boxes of crayons. Each box has 8 crayons. How many crayons does Dave have in all?

   Answer: _____ crayons

4. For a party, Karen bought 3 packages of balloons. Each package had 5 balloons. How many balloons did she buy in all?

   Answer: _____ balloons

5. Write your own multiplication story. Then draw pictures or use counters to find the answer.

   _____

   _____

   Answer: _____

Practice Set 42

Use with or after
Lesson 6·9

MRB
34–35
112–113

For each problem • make an array
• fill in the number model
• write the answer

Example The garden has
5 rows of flowers. Each
row has 3 flowers. How
many flowers are there?

● ● ● · · · · · · · · ·
● ● ● · · · · · · · · ·
● ● ● · · · · · · · · ·
● ● ● · · · · · · · · ·
● ● ● · · · · · · · · ·

$\underline{\ 5\ } \times \underline{\ 3\ } = \underline{\ 15\ }$

There are __15__ flowers
in the garden.

1. The gameboard has
3 rows. Each row has
6 squares. How many
squares are there?

_____ × _____ = _____

There are _____ squares
on the gameboard.

2. The calculator has 4 rows
of keys. There are 5 keys
in each row. How many
keys are there?

_____ × _____ = _____

There are _____ keys
on the calculator.

3. Each page of the picture
album has 2 rows of
pictures. Each row has
3 pictures. How many
pictures are on each page?

_____ × _____ = _____

There are _____ pictures
on each page.

Solve.

4. $10 = 3 +$ _____

5. _____ $+ 28 = 40$

6. $45 +$ _____ $= 70$

7. $90 = 67 +$ _____

Unit

Name	Date	Time

Practice Set 43

Use with or after
Lesson 6·10

Draw pictures or use counters to find the answers.

1. 20 cents shared equally ...

by 4 people	by 5 people	by 6 people
_____ ¢ per person	_____ ¢ per person	_____ ¢ per person
_____ ¢ remaining	_____ ¢ remaining	_____ ¢ remaining

2. 35 books shared equally ...

by 5 children	by 6 children
_____ books per child	_____ books per child
_____ books remaining	_____ books remaining
by 7 children	**by 8 children**
_____ books per child	_____ books per child
_____ books remaining	_____ books remaining

Count by 2s.

3. _900_, _902_, _____, _____, _____, _____, _____, _____, _____

4. _389_, _____, _____, _____, _____, _____, _401_, _____, _____, _____

Count by 10s.

5. _610_, _620_, _____, _____, _____, _____, _____, _____, _____, _____

6. _716_, _706_, _____, _____, _____, _____, _____, _____, _____, _____

43

Practice Set 44

Use with or after
Lesson 7·1

MRB
6–7
28–29

801	802	803							810
811			814					819	
	822				826	827			830
		833		835				839	840
			844				848		
851					856				
	862							869	
871									880
		883	884			887			
891	892				896		898		900
	902	903						909	
	912				916				920

1. Fill in all of the missing numbers on the grid.

2. Now start at 804 and count by 10s.
   Put an **X** over each number as you count.

3. Now circle three *odd* numbers on the grid.

Now use the grid to find these four sums:

4. 803 + 10 = _____

5. _____ = 30 + 844

6. _____ = 862 + 40

7. 40 + 869 = _____

44

Practice Set 45

Use with or after
Lesson 7·2

For Problems 1–6, fill in the missing number.

Unit
chickens

1. $50 = 42 + $ _____   2. $90 = $ _____ $ + 89$

3. $64 + $ _____ $ = 70$ 4. $30 = 27 + $ _____

5. $35 + $ _____ $ = 40$ 6. $53 + $ _____ $ = 60$

601	602	603		△	□	607	608	609	610
611				615		○			620
621	622	□			626			△	
	632	633		△		637			640
	642		△				648	649	△
651	○			655			○		660
		663			□			669	○
671			674			677	678		
△		683			686			689	△
	692			□				699	△
	702				706				
711		713				○			720

For Problems 7–12, draw the shape (△, ○, □, or △) for the number.

7. 618 _____   8. 695 _____   9. 666 _____

10. 681 _____   11. 700 _____   12. 717 _____

45

Practice Set 46

**Use with or after
Lesson 7-3**

MRB
28–30
116–118

Add.

Unit
balloons

1. $18 + 7 + 11 =$ _____

2. $13 + 19 + 2 =$ _____

3.
$$\begin{array}{r} 20 \\ 12 \\ + \ 6 \\ \hline \end{array}$$

4.
$$\begin{array}{r} 17 \\ 9 \\ + 18 \\ \hline \end{array}$$

5.
$$\begin{array}{r} 5 \\ 13 \\ + \ 8 \\ \hline \end{array}$$

6.
$$\begin{array}{r} 16 \\ 14 \\ + \ 4 \\ \hline \end{array}$$

Use your calculator to find the answer.

Example

  Enter 24.

  Change to 50.

  Add or subtract? _*add*_

  How much? _*26*_

7. Enter 90.

  Change to 67.

  Add or subtract? _____

  How much? _____

8. Enter 70.

  Change to 22.

  Add or subtract? _____

  How much? _____

9. Enter 48.

  Change to 80.

  Add or subtract? _____

  How much? _____

Name _____ Date _____ Time _____

Practice Set 47

Use with or after
Lesson 7·4

MRB
25 37
107–111

Fill in each table.

1.
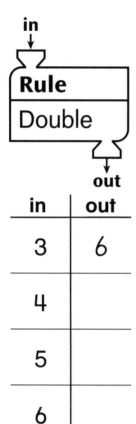

in

Rule
Double

out

in	out
3	6
4	
5	
6	

2.
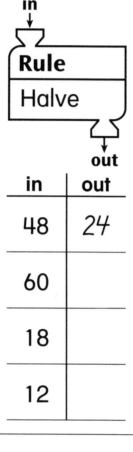

in

Rule
Halve

out

in	out
48	24
60	
18	
12	

Solve.

Animal Measurements

Eagle	**Beaver**	**Raccoon**	**Koala**
length 26 in.	length 30 in.	weight 25 lb	weight 20 lb

3. How much longer is the beaver than the eagle? _____ in. longer

4. How much do the koala and the raccoon weigh together? _____ lb

Practice Set 48

Use with or after
Lesson 7·5

MRB
27
34–36 71

Read the scale. Tell the weight.

1.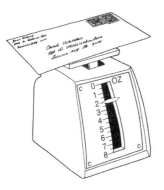

2.

3.

_____ ounces (oz)   _____ pounds (lb)   _____ pounds (lb)

Draw pictures or use counters to find the answers.

4. 15 toys shared
equally by 4 friends

_____ toys per friend

_____ toys remaining

5. 29 bones shared
equally by 9 dogs

_____ bones per dog

_____ bones remaining

Find the missing number.

6. $59 = \underline{\hspace{1cm}} + 9$

7. $\underline{\hspace{1cm}} + 40 = 63$

8. $\underline{\hspace{1cm}} + 60 = 72$

9. $93 = 50 + \underline{\hspace{1cm}}$

10. $70 + \underline{\hspace{1cm}} = 99$

11. $55 = \underline{\hspace{1cm}} + 20$

Practice Set 49

Use with or after
Lesson 7·7

Use this list of numbers to answer each question below:

> **Numbers of People in Second Graders' Families**
>
> 2 5 3 4 6 5 3 3 4 4 2 7 3 5 4 2 4 4 5 3 6 4 3 6 5

1. How many families are shown on the list? _____

2. What is the greatest number of people
   in a second grader's family? _____

3. What is the least? _____

4. Rewrite the numbers in order from least to greatest:

   _____

   _____

5. How many families have 3 people? _____

6. What is the middle, or **median,** value
   shown on the list? _____

Solve.

7. A pencil costs 8¢. A crayon costs 4¢.
   How much do they cost together? _____

8. Gum costs $0.10. Candy costs $0.06.
   How much more does gum cost? _____ more

Practice Set 50

Use with or after
Lesson 7·8

Use the frequency table to answer each question.

Heights of Second Graders

Height (in.)	Frequency	
	Tallies	**Number**
42	///	3
43	##//	5
44	##// /	6
45	##// ///	8
46	//	2

1. How many second graders' heights are shown in the table?

   _____

2. What is the middle, or **median,** value shown in the table?

   _____

Solve.

3. How many dots are in this array? Count by 3s.

   : : : : : : : : :
   : : : : : : : : :
   : : : : : : : : :

   _____ dots

4. Describe this array:

   : : : : : :
   : : : : : :

   _____ by _____

Find the difference between the temperatures.

5. 40°F and 64°F

   _____

6. 29°C and 18°C

   _____

7. 92°F and 57°F

   _____

8. 11°C and 45°C

   _____

50

Practice Set 51

Write 2 fractions for each shape.

Example	1.	2.

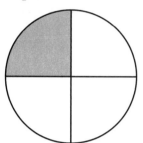

4 equal parts

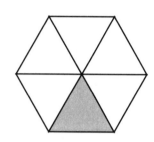

6 equal parts

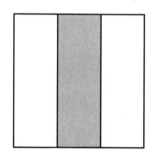

3 equal parts

part shaded $= \dfrac{1}{4}$ part shaded $= \dfrac{}{}$ part shaded $= \dfrac{}{}$

part unshaded $= \dfrac{3}{4}$ part unshaded $= \dfrac{}{}$ part unshaded $= \dfrac{}{}$

Write the missing numbers.

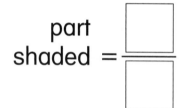

Unit

snakes

3. $80 + \underline{\hphantom{00}} = 92$ **4.** $87 = \underline{\hphantom{00}} + 10$

$70 + \underline{\hphantom{00}} = 92$ $77 = \underline{\hphantom{00}} + 10$

$60 + \underline{\hphantom{00}} = 92$ $67 = \underline{\hphantom{00}} + 10$

$50 + \underline{\hphantom{00}} = 92$ $57 = \underline{\hphantom{00}} + 10$

$40 + \underline{\hphantom{00}} = 92$ $47 = \underline{\hphantom{00}} + 10$

$30 + \underline{\hphantom{00}} = 92$ $37 = \underline{\hphantom{00}} + 10$

Practice Set 52

Use with or after
Lesson 8·2

Label each part of each shape.

Example

$\frac{1}{6}$	$\frac{1}{6}$	$\frac{1}{6}$
$\frac{1}{6}$	$\frac{1}{6}$	$\frac{1}{6}$

1.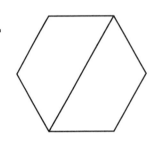

2.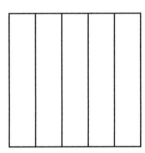

3.

4.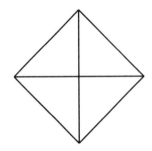

5.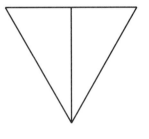

Count by 3s.

Unit

buttons

6. _82_, _85_, ____, ____, ____, ____

7. _216_, ____, ____, _225_, ____, ____, ____, ____, ____, ____

8. _803_, ____, ____, ____, ____, ____, ____, ____, ____, _830_

Find each sum.

9.   29
        + 4
        ___

10.   65
        + 9
        ___

11.   37
        + 6
        ___

12.   52
        + 7
        ___

13.   49
        + 8
        ___

Practice Set 53

Write the fraction for the shaded part.

Example

$$\frac{1}{4}$$

1.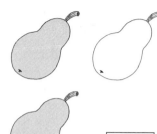

2.

3.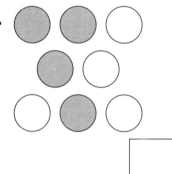

4.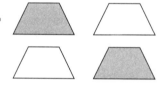

5.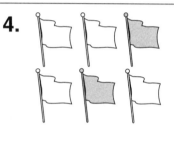

Count back by 10s.

6. 670, 660, ____, ____, ____, ____, ____, ____, 590, ____

7. 286, 276, ____, ____, ____, ____, ____, ____, ____, 196

8. 524, ____, ____, 494, ____, ____, ____, ____, ____, ____

9. 937, ____, ____, ____, ____, ____, 877, ____, ____, ____

Practice Set 54

Use with or after
Lesson 8·6

Write >, <, or = .

1. This is ONE:

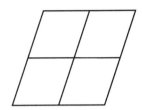

$\frac{2}{4}$ ☐ $\frac{3}{4}$ $\frac{1}{2}$ ☐ $\frac{2}{4}$ $\frac{3}{4}$ ☐ $\frac{1}{4}$

2. This is ONE:

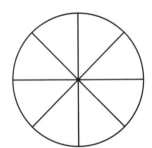

$\frac{5}{8}$ ☐ $\frac{3}{4}$ $\frac{2}{4}$ ☐ $\frac{3}{8}$ $\frac{1}{2}$ ☐ $\frac{4}{8}$

3. This is ONE:

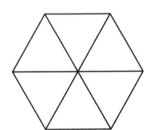

$\frac{3}{6}$ ☐ $\frac{4}{6}$ $\frac{1}{2}$ ☐ $\frac{3}{6}$ $\frac{1}{3}$ ☐ $\frac{1}{6}$

Write the missing number.

Unit
feet

4. _____ + 5 = 10

5. 10 = _____ + 2

6. 80 = 53 + _____

7. 14 + _____ = 30

8. _____ + 59 = 90

9. 60 = _____ + 47

Practice Set 55

Solve each problem.

1. 5 apples were in a tree. 2 apples fell to the ground. What fraction of the apples stayed in the tree?

   _____

2. Eight roses grew in a garden. $\frac{1}{4}$ of them were picked and put in a vase. How many roses are in the vase?

   _____

Add or subtract. Show your work in the workspace.

3.	48 + 31	Answer

4.	67 − 49	Answer

5.	23 + 58	Answer

6.	84 + 15	Answer

7.	92 − 51	Answer

8.	74 − 36	Answer

Practice Set 56

Reminder:
10 cm = 1 dm

About how many decimeters long?

1.

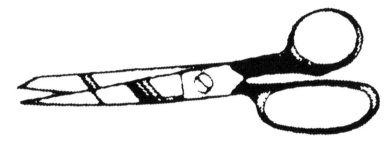

about _____ decimeter(s) long

2.

about _____ decimeter(s) long

**Solve each problem.
You can use counters or draw pictures.**

3. There are 4 shelves on the wall. Each shelf holds 7 books. How many books are there in all?

4. Pat bought 5 packs of juice boxes. Each pack holds 6 boxes. How many juice boxes did he buy?

Answer: _____ books

Answer: _____ juice boxes

Practice Set 57

MRB
28–35
65–66

How much is shaded? Write a fraction.

1.

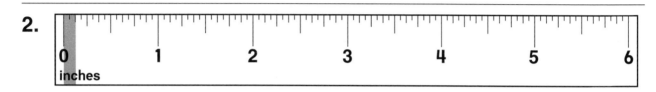

_____ in.

2.

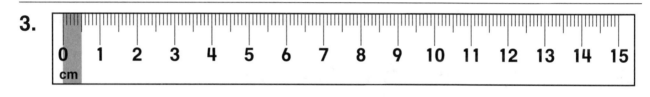

_____ in.

3.

_____ cm

Add or subtract. Show your work in the workspace.

4.	36 + 19	Answer	5.	53 + 27	Answer	6.	96 − 58	Answer

57

Practice Set 58

Use with or after
Lesson 9·4

Measure the perimeter to the nearest $\frac{1}{2}$ cm.

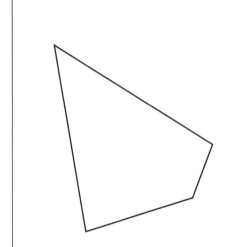

1. Perimeter: _____ cm

2. Perimeter: _____ cm

Color the part or parts to match the fraction.

Example

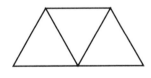

$\frac{1}{2}$

3.

$\frac{1}{3}$

4.

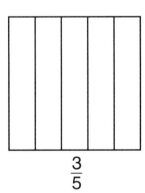

$\frac{3}{5}$

5.

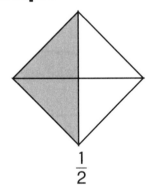

$\frac{2}{3}$

6.

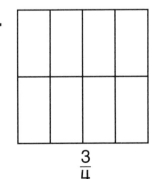

$\frac{3}{4}$

7.

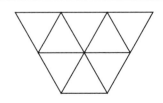

$\frac{1}{2}$

Practice Set 59

Circle the measurement tool you would use.

1.

2.

Circle the unit of measure you would use.

3. 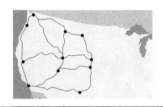   miles   feet

4.    centimeters   meters

Use your calculator to find the answers.

5. Enter 39.

Change to 70.

Add or subtract? _____

How much? _____

6. Enter 90.

Change to 24.

Add or subtract? _____

How much? _____

7. Sue entered a number in her calculator.
Then she changed the number to 50
by adding 13. What number did she enter *first*? _____

Practice Set 60

Use with or after
Lesson 9·7

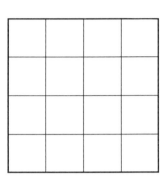

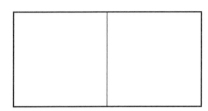

1. **Area:** _____ square cm

   Perimeter: _____ cm

2. **Area:** _____ square in.

   Perimeter: _____ in.

For each multiplication story
- **draw a picture or diagram**
- **fill in the number model**
- **write the answer**

3. Ruth cut 3 large sandwiches into 3 pieces each. How many pieces does she have in all?

4. Ryan has 3 fishbowls with 4 fish in each bowl. How many fish does he have in all?

Number model:

____ × ____ = ____

Answer: ____ _____
           (unit)

Number model:

____ × ____ = ____

Answer: ____ _____
           (unit)

Practice Set 61

Circle the correct amount.

1.		$\frac{1}{2}$ cup	1 quart
2.		1 pint	$\frac{1}{2}$ gallon
3.		$\frac{1}{2}$ liter	1 liter

Write the turn-around addition facts.

Example

4, 11, 7 $\underline{4} + \underline{7} = \underline{11}$ $\underline{7} + \underline{4} = \underline{11}$

4. 12, 3, 9   ___ + ___ = ___   ___ + ___ = ___

5. 13, 9, 22   ___ + ___ = ___   ___ + ___ = ___

6. 7, 6, 13   ___ + ___ = ___   ___ + ___ = ___

7. 17, 6, 23   ___ + ___ = ___   ___ + ___ = ___

Name _____ Date _____ Time _____

Practice Set 62

Use with or after
Lesson 9·9

MRB
66 71

1. How much does half a bag weigh?

_____

2. How much do 2 bags weigh?

_____

FLOUR

5 kg

Measure each object to the nearest half-centimeter.

Example

0 1 2 3 4 5 6 7 8 9 10 11 12 13 14 15
cm

Measurement: about _____ $12 \frac{1}{2}$ cm _____

3.

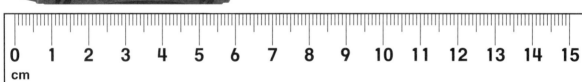

0 1 2 3 4 5 6 7 8 9 10 11 12 13 14 15
cm

Measurement: about _____

4.

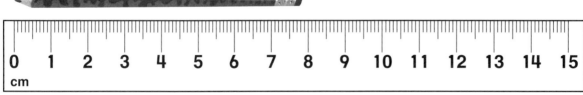

0 1 2 3 4 5 6 7 8 9 10 11 12 13 14 15
cm

Measurement: about _____

Practice Set 63

Use with or after
Lesson 10·1

Show each amount of money two different ways.

Use Qs, Ds, Ns, Ps, and $1 s.

1.  a lb of grapes for 99¢

2. a jar of peanut butter for $1.29

Count back by 2s.

3. <u>80</u>, <u>78</u>, ____, ____, ____, ____, ____, ____, ____, <u>62</u>

4. <u>59</u>, <u>57</u>, ____, ____, ____, <u>49</u>, ____, ____, ____, ____

5. <u>134</u>, <u>132</u>, ____, ____, ____, ____, ____, ____, ____, <u>116</u>

6. <u>251</u>, ____, ____, <u>245</u>, ____, ____, ____, ____, ____, ____

Practice Set 64

Use with or after
Lesson 10-2

MRB
14
88–89

Match equal amounts.

1. $\frac{1}{2}$ dime $0.01

2. penny $\frac{1}{10}$ dollar

3. dime   nickel

4. $\frac{1}{4}$ dollar   quarter

Color the part or parts to match the fraction.

5.

$\frac{3}{5}$ are red.

6.
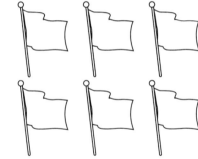

$\frac{1}{2}$ are blue.

7.
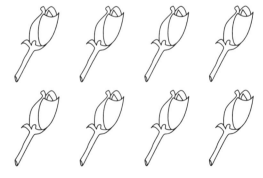

$\frac{1}{4}$ are pink.

8.

$\frac{2}{3}$ are orange.

Practice Set 65

Use with or after
Lesson 10·3

Use your calculator. Enter each amount of money. Then write what your calculator shows.

Enter	Display
47¢	0.47
1. $1.32	
2. $0.98	
3. 9¢	

Enter	Display
4. 65¢	
5. $2.50	
6. $0.04	
7. $4.09	

Use these numbers to answer the questions below:

954   127   923   962   753   347

8. Which numbers have 3 ones? _____

9. Which numbers have 5 tens? _____

10. Which numbers have 9 hundreds? _____

11. Which *even* number has 6 tens? _____

12. Which *odd* number has 1 hundred? _____

13. Which *even* numbers have 9 hundreds? _____

14. Which *odd* number has 9 hundreds? _____

Practice Set 66

Going to Get Groceries

American Cheese $1.49	Saltines 69¢
Wheat Bread 99¢	Hamburger Buns 69¢
Potato Chips 89¢	Mayonnaise $1.99
Ketchup $1.09	Ice Cream $2.49
Watermelon $2.99	Yogurt $2.09
Grape Jelly $1.69	Lunch Meat $1.39

You want to buy the items listed below. *Estimate* the total cost, and then *find* the total cost.

Items	Estimated Cost	Total Cost
1. Potato Chips	about $____._____	$____._____
Yogurt		$____._____
		$____._____ Total
2. American Cheese	about $____._____	$____._____
Grape Jelly		$____._____
		$____._____ Total
3. Mayonnaise	about $____._____	$____._____
Wheat Bread		$____._____
Watermelon		$____._____
		$____._____ Total

Practice Set 67

Use your calculator to solve each problem.

Items Bought	Total Cost	Amount You Paid With	Amount of Change
1. Pen: $1.89	$___.___	$5.00	$___.___
Notebook: $2.40	$___.___		
Total:	$___.___		
2. Crayons: $1.20	$___.___	$10.00	$___.___
Game: $6.85	$___.___		
Total:	$___.___		
3. Key Chain: $1.60	$___.___	$10.00	$___.___
Toy Car: $4.09	$___.___		
Stickers: $1.14	$___.___		
Candy: $0.55	$___.___		
Total:	$___.___		

Write the missing number.

4. ____ + 68 = 70

5. 40 = 36 + ____

6. 72 + ____ = 80

7. ____ + 49 = 50

8. 20 = ____ + 11

9. ____ = 85 + 15

Practice Set 68

Use with or after
Lesson 10·8

Write the amount.

1.

$ _____ . _____

2.

$ _____ . _____

Complete each table.

3.
in ↓

Rule
+ 7

out ↓

in	out
5	12
	16
	8
	13

4.
in ↓

Rule
− 5

out ↓

in	out
	10
	13
	17
	45

5.
in ↓

Rule
+ $0.10

out ↓

in	out
	$0.20
	$0.35
	$0.18
	$0.12

Practice Set 69

Write the number.

1. four thousand, two hundred ten _____

2. four thousand, twelve _____

3. four hundred one _____

4. ten thousand, six hundred nine _____

5. fourteen thousand, one hundred _____

6. forty thousand, ninety-eight _____

Add or subtract. Show your work in the workspace.

7. $\begin{array}{r} 77 \\ -\ 28 \end{array}$	Answer	8. $\begin{array}{r} 51 \\ +\ 29 \end{array}$	Answer	9. $\begin{array}{r} 89 \\ +\ 12 \end{array}$	Answer
10. $\begin{array}{r} 36 \\ -\ 34 \end{array}$	Answer	11. $\begin{array}{r} 57 \\ +\ 29 \end{array}$	Answer	12. $\begin{array}{r} 45 \\ +\ 69 \end{array}$	Answer

Practice Set 70

Use with or after
Lesson 10·11

Solve.

1. $17 - (8 + 5) =$ _____

2. $24 - (6 + 9) =$ _____

3. $28 + (6 - 2) =$ _____

4. $13 + (10 - 9) =$ _____

5. $16 + (27 - 17) =$ _____

6. $18 + (16 - 9) =$ _____

Measure to the nearest half-inch.

Example

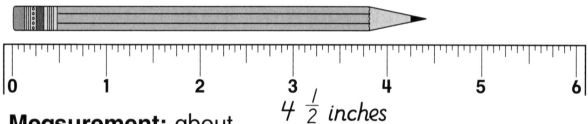

Measurement: about _____ $4\frac{1}{2}$ inches _____

7.

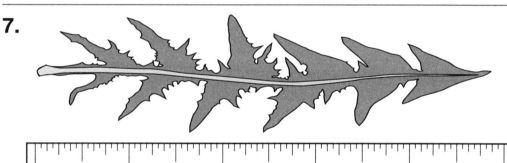

Measurement: about _____

8.

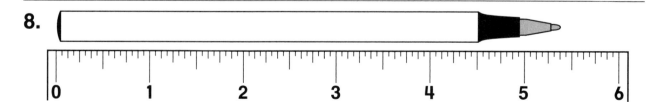

Measurement: about _____

70

Practice Set 71

Use with or after
Lesson 11·1

1. A bag of apples costs $5.21. A box of crackers costs $3.29. How much do they cost together?

Estimated Cost:

_____

Total Cost:

_____

2. A box of peaches costs $7.11. A bag of oranges costs $4.69. How much do they cost together?

Estimated Cost:

_____

Total Cost:

_____

Complete each table.

3.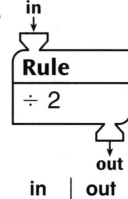

in	out
1	4
	8
	16
	12
5	

4.

in	out
4	2
	3
	10
12	
	7

5.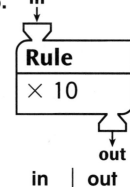

in	out
1	10
	40
3	
	60
5	

71

Practice Set 72

1. A bag of apples costs $5.21. A bag of oranges costs $4.69. How much more do the oranges cost?

   Estimated Difference:

   _____

   Actual Difference:

   _____

2. A bag of chips costs $3.29. A box of pretzels costs $2.25. How much less do the pretzels cost?

   Estimated Difference:

   _____

   Actual Difference:

   _____

Tell what each of the digits stands for. Be careful!

Example 4,703

4 _____ *thousands* _____

7 _____ *hundreds* _____

0 _____ *tens* _____

3 _____ *ones* _____

3. 2,865

6 _____

8 _____

5 _____

2 _____

4. 1,639

9 _____

1 _____

3 _____

6 _____

5. 3,052

5 _____

0 _____

2 _____

3 _____

Practice Set 73

Use with or after
Lesson 11·4

For each multiplication story
- **draw a picture, diagram, or array**
- **fill in the number model**
- **write the answer**

1. Four cars go to the beach. Each car has 5 people inside. How many people go to the beach?

Number model:

_____ × _____ = _____

Answer: _____ _____
            (unit)

2. Maria has 9 pairs of shoes in her closet. How many shoes does she have in all?

Number model:

_____ × _____ = _____

Answer: _____ _____
            (unit)

Write the number.

Unit
snowflakes

3. four thousand, twenty-four _____

4. three thousand, eight hundred fifty-two _____

5. seven hundred fifty-seven _____

6. six thousand, two hundred forty-three _____

7. nine thousand, six hundred fourteen _____

Practice Set 74

For each division story
- **draw a picture, diagram, or array**
- **fill in the number model**
- **write the answer**

1. Laura has 17 flowers.
   She puts 3 flowers in each vase.
   How many vases does she fill?

   _____ ÷ _____ → _____ R _____

   _____ vases have flowers in them.

   _____ flowers are left over.

2. Five children share 25 crackers equally.
   How many crackers does each child get?

   _____ ÷ _____ → _____ R _____

   Each child gets _____ crackers.

   _____ crackers are left over.

3. Thirty oranges are divided equally among 6 bags.
   How many oranges are put in each bag?

   _____ ÷ _____ → _____ R _____

   _____ oranges are put in each bag.

   _____ oranges are left over.

Practice Set 75

Use with or after Lesson 11·6

MRB 108–113

Draw an array to find the product.

1. $4 \times 3 =$ _____

. . .
. . .
. . .
. . .

2. $2 \times 9 =$ _____

3. $3 \times 7 =$ _____

4. $1 \times 8 =$ _____

5. $6 \times 3 =$ _____

6. $5 \times 4 =$ _____

Solve.

7. On a field trip, the second grade class rode 38 miles on a bus in the morning. In the afternoon, the children rode 27 miles. How many miles did they travel in all?

_____

8. How many more miles did the second grade class travel in the morning than in the afternoon?

_____

75

Practice Set 76

Find the product.

Unit
stars

1. $0 \times 7 =$ _____

2. $1 \times 6 =$ _____

3. $9 \times 0 =$ _____

4. $2 \times 1 =$ _____

5. $10 \times 0 =$ _____

6. $0 \times 50 =$ _____

7. $72 \times 1 =$ _____

8. $123 \times 0 =$ _____

Add or subtract. Show your work in the workspace.

9.
$$\begin{array}{r} 87 \\ - 49 \\ \hline \end{array}$$
Answer

10.
$$\begin{array}{r} 16 \\ 23 \\ + 12 \\ \hline \end{array}$$
Answer

11.
$$\begin{array}{r} 64 \\ - 35 \\ \hline \end{array}$$
Answer

12.
$$\begin{array}{r} 49 \\ + 53 \\ \hline \end{array}$$
Answer

13.
$$\begin{array}{r} 89 \\ - 44 \\ \hline \end{array}$$
Answer

14.
$$\begin{array}{r} 53 \\ 28 \\ + 39 \\ \hline \end{array}$$
Answer

Practice Set 77

Write the fact family for the Fact Triangle.

Example

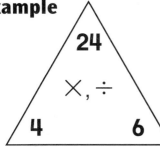

_4_ × _6_ = _24_

_6_ × _4_ = _24_

_24_ ÷ _4_ = _6_

_24_ ÷ _6_ = _4_

1.

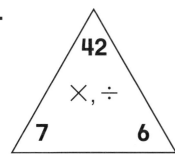

___ × ___ = ___

___ × ___ = ___

___ ÷ ___ = ___

___ ÷ ___ = ___

2.

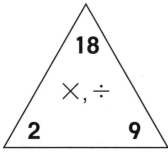

___ × ___ = ___

___ × ___ = ___

___ ÷ ___ = ___

___ ÷ ___ = ___

3.

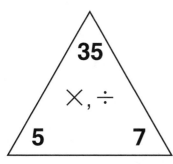

___ × ___ = ___

___ × ___ = ___

___ ÷ ___ = ___

___ ÷ ___ = ___

For each number below:

- **circle** the digit in the hundreds place

- **underline** the digit in the thousands place

- **put an X** over the digit in the tens place

- **draw a square** around the digit in the ones place

Example 9 2 X 6

4. 5 6 1 7

5. 2 0 4 7

6. 8 3 9 3

7. 1 0 2 0 8

8. 1 2 5 8 1

9. 1 6 2 1 7

Practice Set 78

Use with or after
Lesson 12-1

1. What month is it? _____

2. How many days are in this month? _____ days

3. Write today's date: _____ _____, _____
   (month)   (day)   (year)

Color the part or parts to match the fraction.

4.

   $\frac{3}{4}$

5.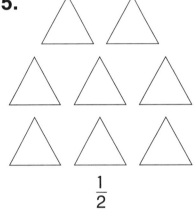

   $\frac{1}{2}$

6.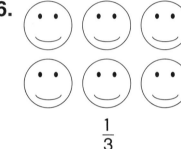

   $\frac{1}{3}$

7.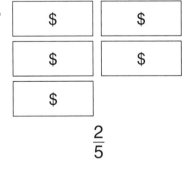

   $\frac{2}{5}$

8.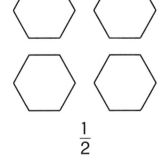

   $\frac{1}{2}$

9.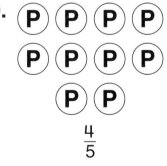

   $\frac{4}{5}$

Practice Set 79

Write the time.

1.

___ : ___

2.

___ : ___

3.

___ : ___

4.

___ : ___

Write the rule. Then fill in the table.

5. in
↓

Rule

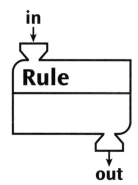

out

in	out
16	32
21	42
	30
12	
17	

6. in
↓

Rule

out

in	out
5	15
4	12
6	
	9
	21

7. in
↓

Rule

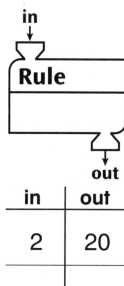

out

in	out
2	20
3	30
7	
	50
8	

Name _____ Date _____ Time _____

Practice Set 80

Multiply. Use your Facts Table on journal page 26.

Unit
dinosaurs

1. 9
    × 7

2. 7
    × 6

3. 6
    × 5

4. 8
    × 8

5. 9
    × 8

6. 7
    × 7

7. 6
    × 9

8. 8
    × 7

Fill in the missing number.

9. 2 ⊚ = _____¢

10. _____ ⊚ = 30¢

11. 10 ⊚ = _____¢

12. _____ ⊚ = 2 ⊚

13. 4 ⊚ = _____¢

14. 5 ⊚ = _____ ⊚

15. _____ ⊚ = 4 ⊚

16. _____¢ = 1 half-dollar

17. 2 [dollar bill] = _____ ⊚

18. 1 half-dollar = _____ ⊚